For my parents, Duncan and Sylvia,
and my sister Yvonne.
Thank you for all your support.
J.McQ.

First published in hardback in 1996
by David Bennett Books Limited, United Kingdom.
First published in paperback in 2000.

ISBN 1 85602 411 3
Printed in Hong Kong.

Cosy Christmas
with Teddy Bear

Jacqueline McQuade

David Bennett Books

Counting the days to Christmas

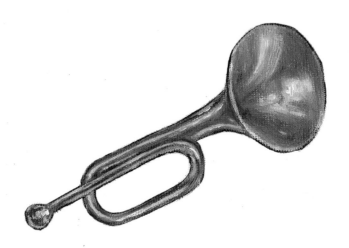

Teddy Bear could hardly wait for Christmas.
Each morning, he would sit with the cat
and cross off another day on the calendar.

Looking in Christmas windows

Teddy liked to go into town with his Dad.
He loved the brightly painted toys in the toy shop window,
especially the yellow aeroplane.

Building
a snowman

*Teddy built a big snowman with coal for eyes
and a carrot nose. He gave him Dad's old hat
and a woolly scarf to keep him warm.*

Writing
a letter
to Santa

"*Dear Santa,*" *wrote Teddy. "I've been a very good bear
this year. For Christmas, I would like the yellow aeroplane
that I saw in the toy shop. I'll leave you a snack by the fireplace:
a carrot for Rudolph and some milk and cookies for you.*"

Singing carols

*One snowy Christmas evening, Mum and Dad
took Teddy carol-singing. They sang his favourite carols
and then went home for hot soup.*

Decorating the tree

Teddy and his Dad decorated the tree together.
Teddy's favourite moment was adding the special star
he'd made the year before to the top of the Christmas tree.

Making Christmas cards

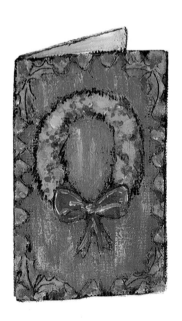

Teddy made two special cards. He drew a tree for Mum and a snowman for Dad. He carefully coloured them in, and then he and the cat signed them with kisses and a paw print.

Wrapping a present

Teddy got some Christmas wrapping paper and a long, silky ribbon. With the cat's help, he remembered how to tie a beautiful big bow.

Hanging up the stocking

It was nearly time for bed, so Teddy hung up his stocking on the mantelpiece where Santa could find it easily and imagined all the things that would be there in the morning.

Looking for Santa's sleigh

*Teddy was so excited he couldn't sleep.
He gazed out into the night,
hoping to see Santa's sleigh.*

Opening presents from Santa

*On Christmas morning, Teddy woke up very early.
His stocking was overflowing with presents,
and there on the top was the yellow aeroplane.*

Giving
a present

"Merry Christmas," said Teddy,
and gave his cat a special present.
"I love you."

Other Jacqueline McQuade Teddy Bear stories for you to enjoy…
all published by David Bennett Books!

Cosy Moments with Teddy Bear

Hardback *ISBN*   1 85602 254 4

Cosy Christmas with Teddy Bear

Hardback *ISBN*   1 85602 253 6
Board Book *ISBN* 1 85602 273 0

Pets' Corner with Teddy Bear

Board Book *ISBN* 1 85602 279 X

Nursery School with Teddy Bear

Board Book *ISBN* 1 85602 280 3

A Baby Sister for Teddy Bear

Hardback *ISBN*   1 85602 363 X
Paperback *ISBN*   1 85602 398 2

Moving House with Teddy Bear

Hardback *ISBN*   1 85602 364 8
Paperback *ISBN*   1 85602 399 0

Available from all good bookshops.